# ASIDE FROM MY COWORKERS

## MY JOB IS FUCKING AWESOME

# TIME TO

# GET SHIT DONE

# SMILE AND PRETEND SHIT IS OKAY

# I AM THE DOG'S BOLLOCKS

# EMPLOYEE*

*****BECAUSE KICKASS MIRACLE WORKER IS NOT AN OFFICIAL JOB TITLE.**

# YOU MUST BE MISTAKING ME FOR SOMEBODY WHO GIVES A SHIT

# YODA BEST

## FUCKER I KNOW

# I'M A SUPER hero

## What's Your Fucking Superpower?

# TODAY I'M JUST A

# MOTHERFUCKING DELIGHT

# I COULD GIVE

# A RAT'S ASS

# I CARE A WHOLE FUCKING LOT

I'M A NICE BASTARD BUT FOR YOU I WILL MAKE A FUCKING EXCEPTION

# I'M FUCKING AWESOME

# I'M DONE HELPING ASSHOLES TODAY

# WHO THE FUCK SAID THIS WOULD BE EASY?

YEAH. BASICALLY I LISTEN TO PEOPLE COMPLAIN.

# WE WILL CONTINUE HAVING MEETINGS UNTIL WE FIND OUT WHY NO FUCKING WORK IS GETTING DONE

# Oh Dear

# I forgot to give a fuck.

I DON'T LIKE MORNING PEOPLE OR MORNINGS OR PEOPLE

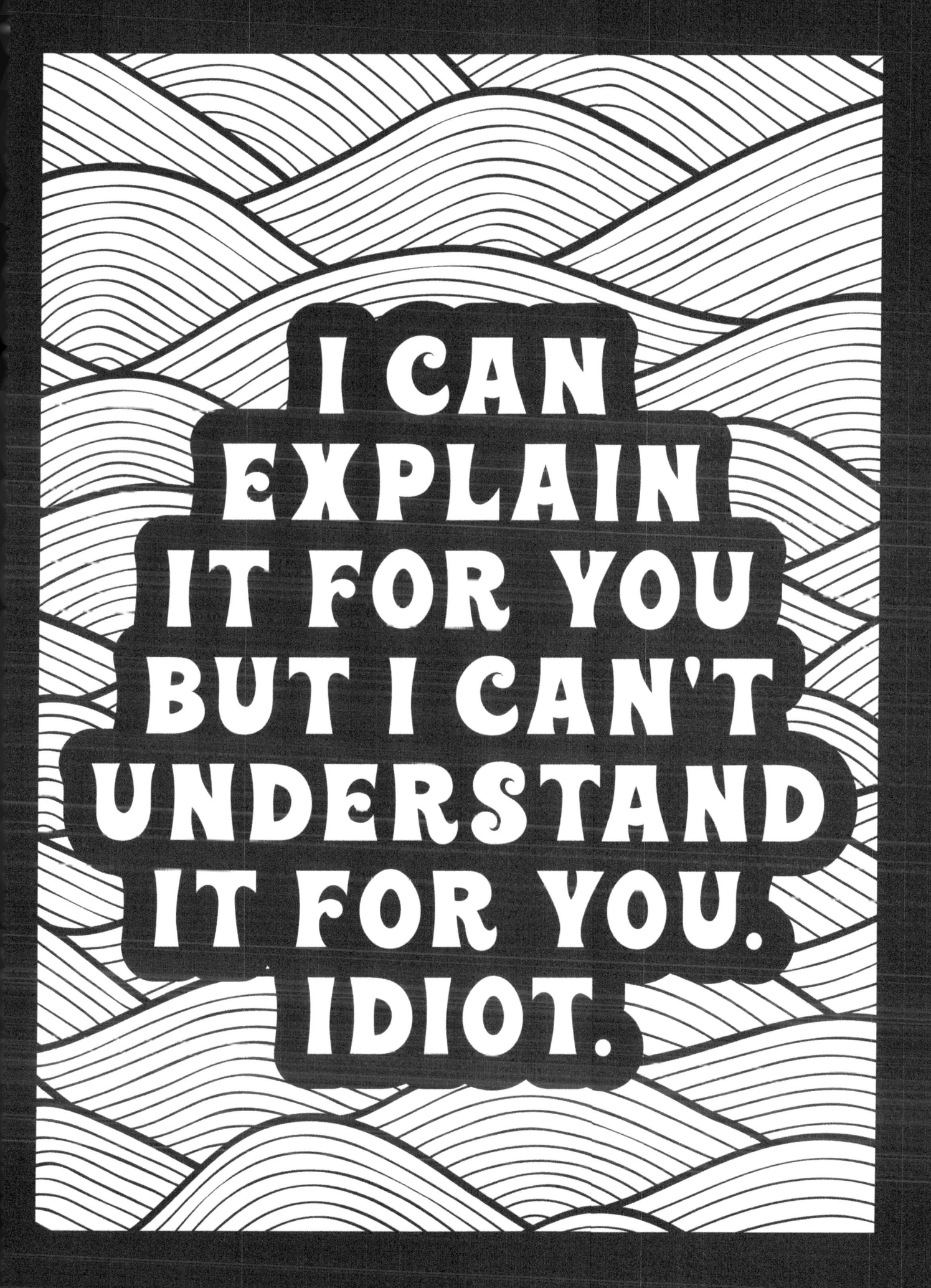

I CAN EXPLAIN IT FOR YOU BUT I CAN'T UNDERSTAND IT FOR YOU. IDIOT.

# KEEP TALKING

## ALL I HEAR ARE THE VOICES IN MY HEAD

I SEARCHED FOR "WHO GIVES A FUCK?"

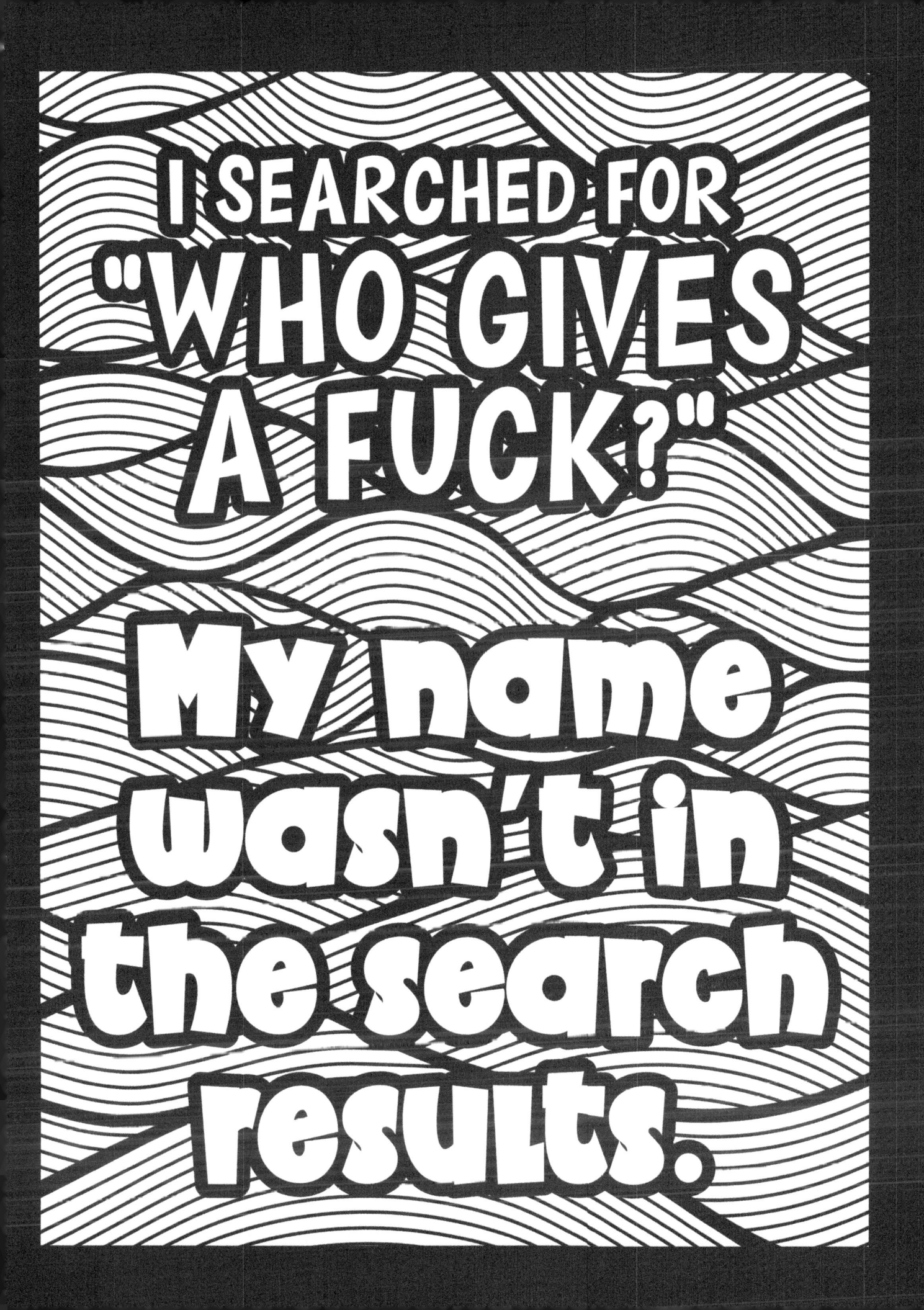

My name wasn't in the search results.

I suck at apologies. So **UNFUCK YOU** Or whatever

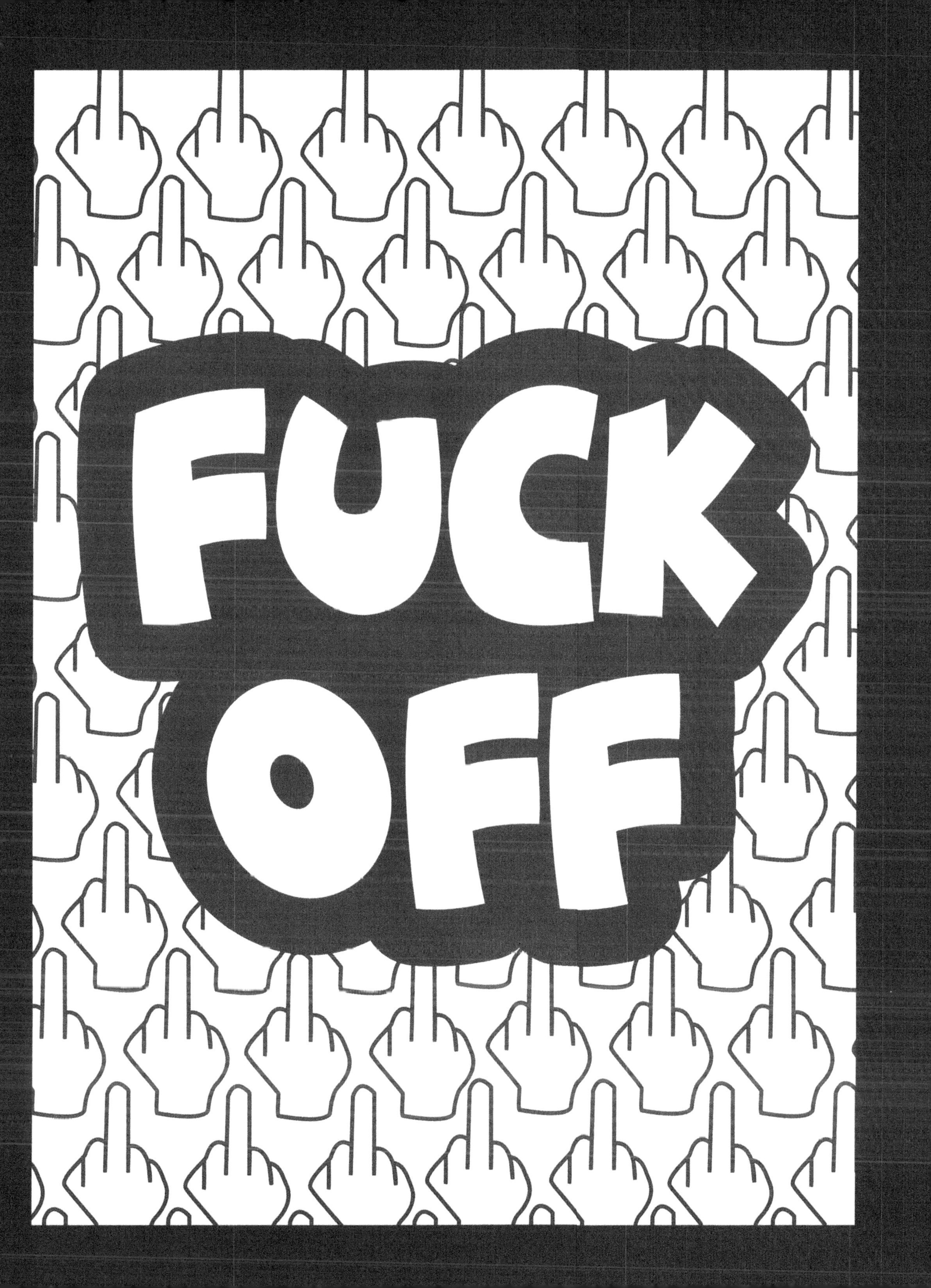
FUCK
OFF

# NO SHiT

I'VE GOT A BAD CASE OF THE FUCK ITS

# FUCK THIS SHIT

# Sack of Shit

# ARE YOU

# FUCKING SERIOUS?

# Sleep Well MiDDLE FiNGER You Have A Big Day Ahead Of You Tomorrow

WHEN I SAY HAVE A NICE **DAY** REMEMBER THAT THE "FUCKER" IS SILENT.

# I WONDER IF LIFE SMOKES ME AFTER IT FUCKS ME

# FUCK OFF
### AND WHEN YOU GET THERE
# FUCK OFF
# AGAIN

# THE PATH OF INNER PEACE BEGINS WITH FOUR WORDS

# NOT MY FUCKING PROBLEM

I'M SORRY WHAT LANGUAGE ARE YOU SPEAKING? IT SOUNDS LIKE BULLSHIT

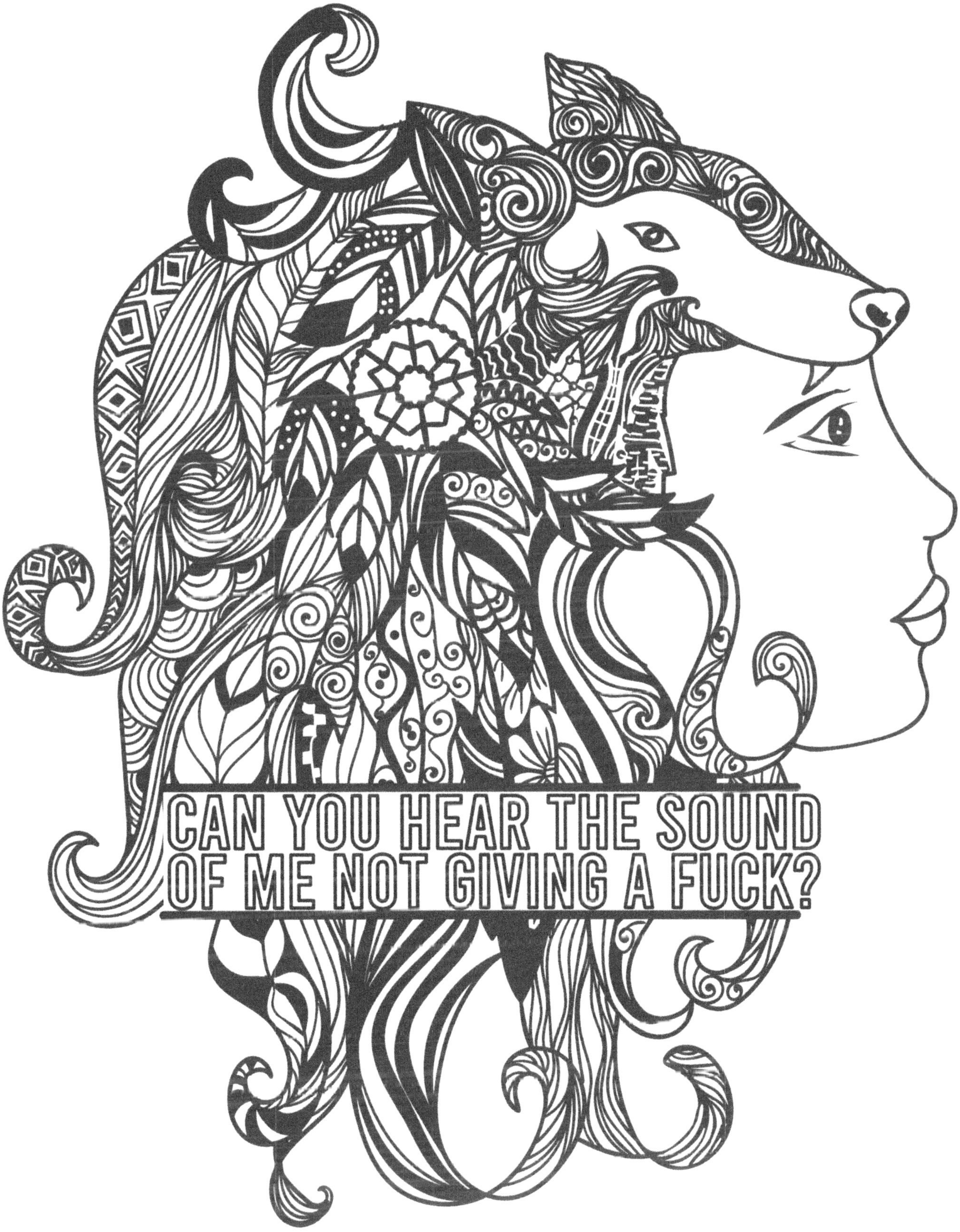
CAN YOU HEAR THE SOUND
OF ME NOT GIVING A FUCK?

LET'S GET THE FUCK
OUT OF HERE

# UTTER BULLSHIT

# SURROUNDED BY BLOODY IDIOTS

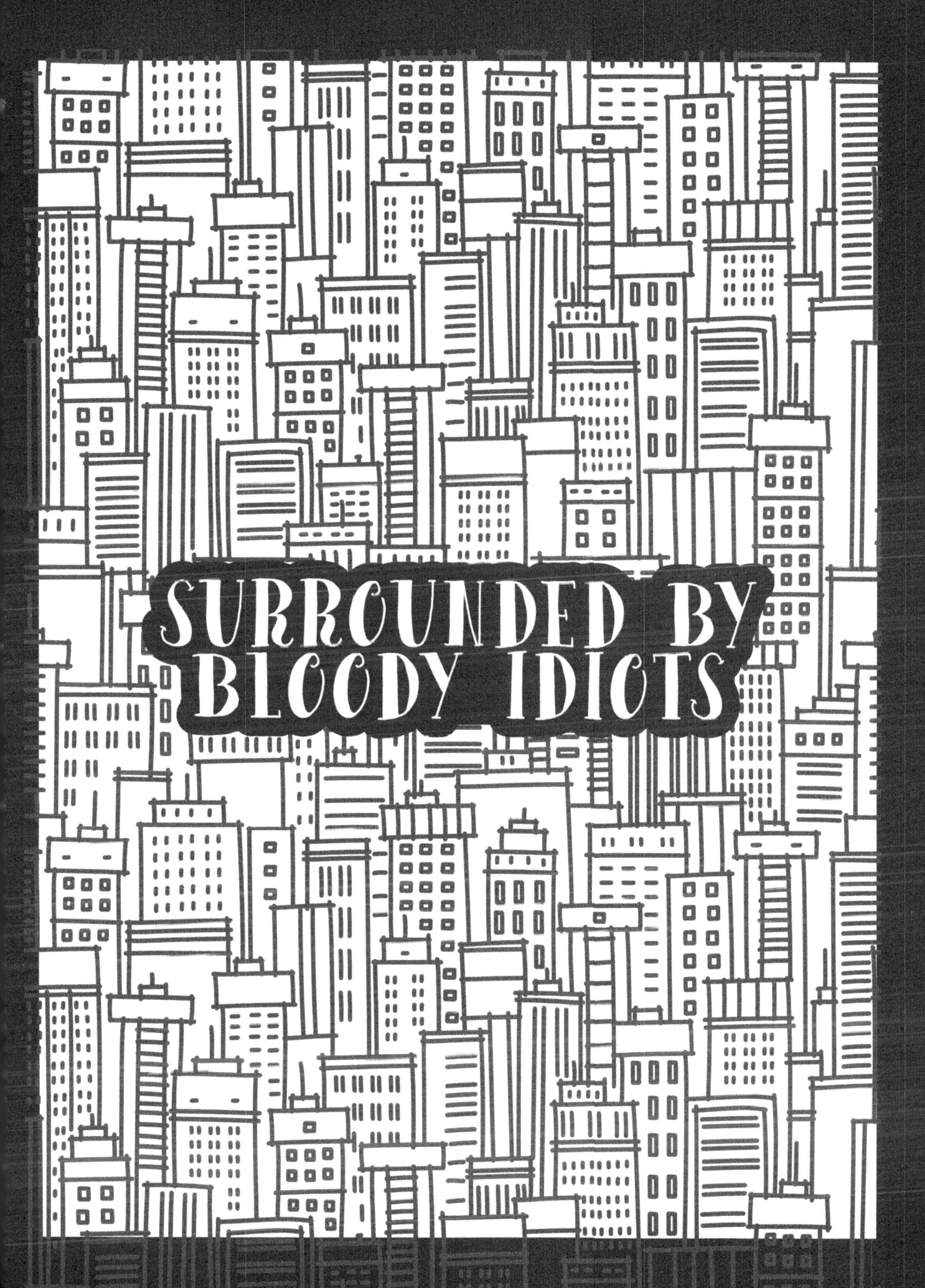

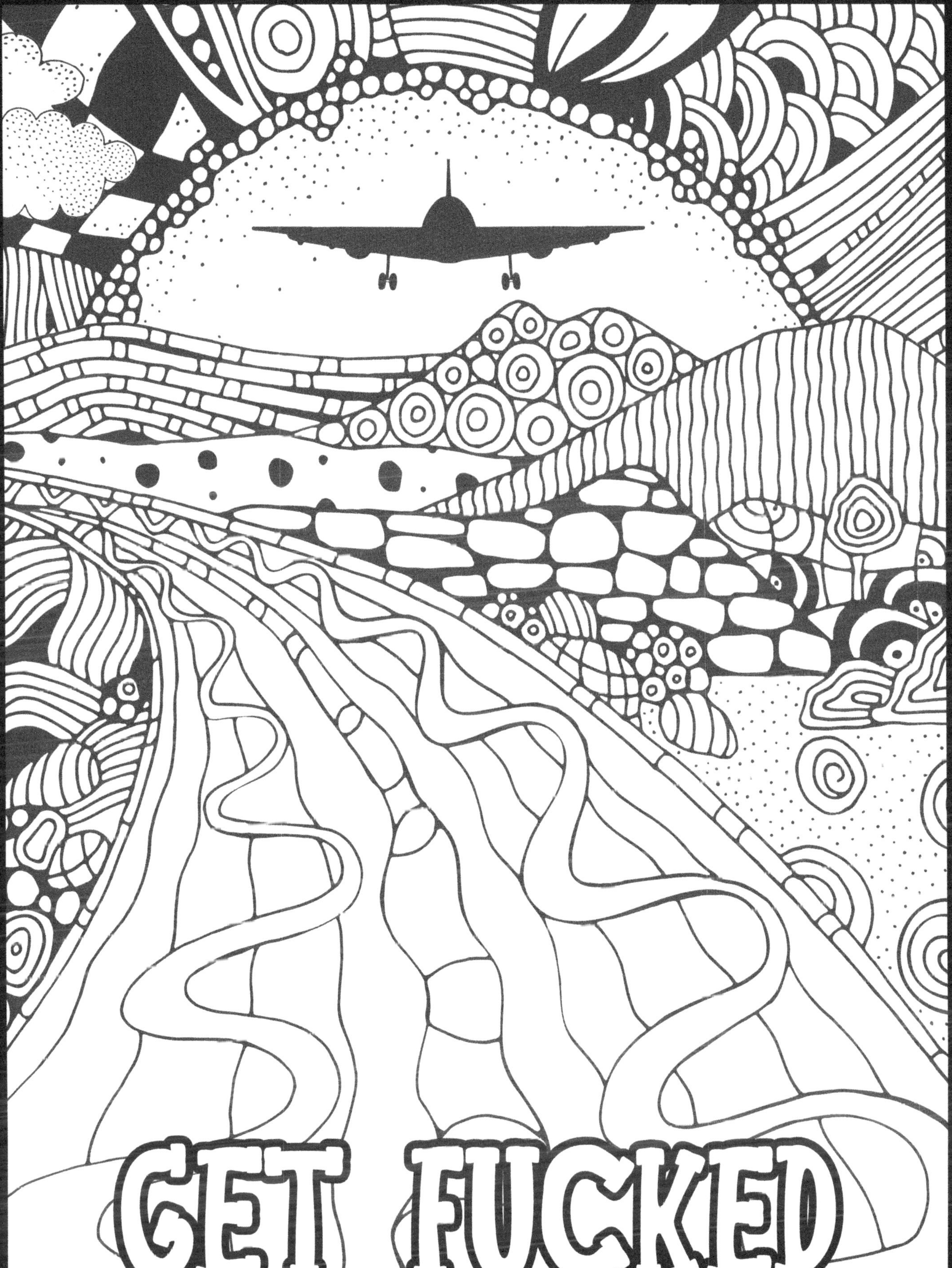
GET FUCKED

# SON OF A BITCH

LEAVE ME THE FUCK ALONE

# SORRY YOU WANKER

## THE DEADLINE FOR COMPLAINTS WAS YESTERDAY

Made in the USA
Coppell, TX
27 April 2021